L'ANGLAIS POUR DÉBUTANTS

I AM LEARNING
ENGLISH

Mots   Verbes   Jeux

THIS ACTIVITY BOOK BELONGS TO :

I can speak english!

GÉNIES JR.

Hi! My name is Sam.
Allô ! Je m'appelle Sam.

I am six.
J'ai six ans.

My name is Lili.
Je m'appelle Lili.

I am seven years old.
J'ai sept ans.

What is your name?
Quel est ton nom ?

How old are you?
Quel âge as-tu ?

Where do you live?
Où vis-tu ?

Draw a portrait of yourself.

Dessine un portrait de toi-même.

Family

Write the word for each family member.

Écris le mot de chaque membre de la famille.

mother • father • sister • brother

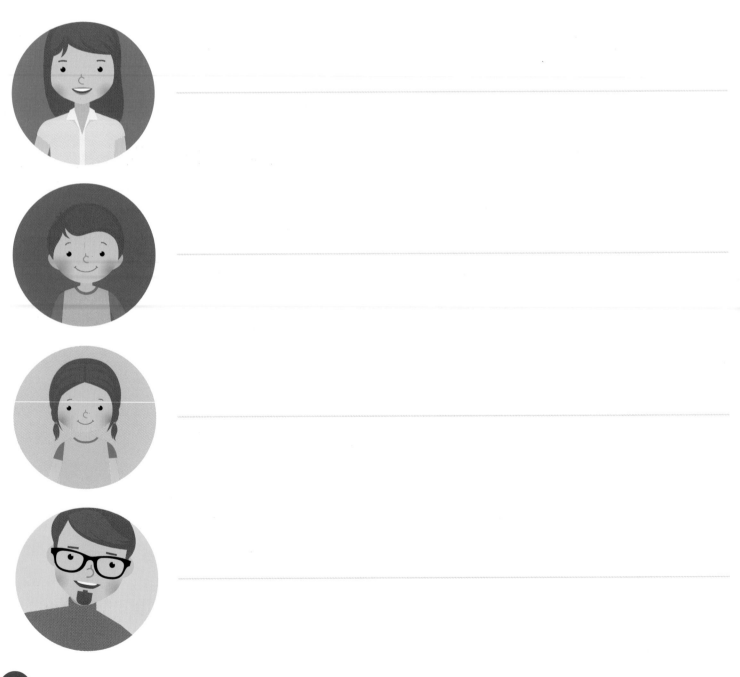

Who is older? The boy or the girl?

Qui est le plus vieux : le garçon ou la fille ?

Who is taller?

Qui est le plus grand ?

Family

Write the word for each family member.

Écris le mot de chaque membre de la famille.

dad • mom • grandpa • grandma • cousin

1 _____   4 _____

2 _____   5 _____

3 _____

Circle the matching pairs, find the two that don't belong.

Relie les jumeaux et entoure les deux enfants qui sont uniques.

Write the color names.

Écris les noms des couleurs.

yellow • green • red • blue • orange • purple

_____

_____

_____

_____

_____

_____

Color in the picture using the color code.

Colorie l'image en suivant le code de couleurs.

a b c d e f

Color the little bear in brown and her dress in pink.

Colorie la petite ourse en brun et ses vêtements en rose.

Color in the drawing using the color code.

Colorie l'image en suivant le code de couleurs.

one two three four five six

Numbers

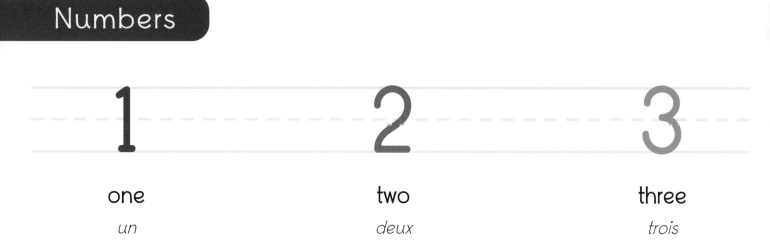

1

one

un

2

two

deux

3

three

trois

Practice writing the number words:

Exerce-toi à écrire le nom des chiffres :

1 _____

2 _____

3 _____

Draw three flowers.

Dessine trois fleurs.

4	5	6
four	five	six
quatre	*cinq*	*six*

Practice writing the number words:

Exerce-toi à écrire le nom des chiffres :

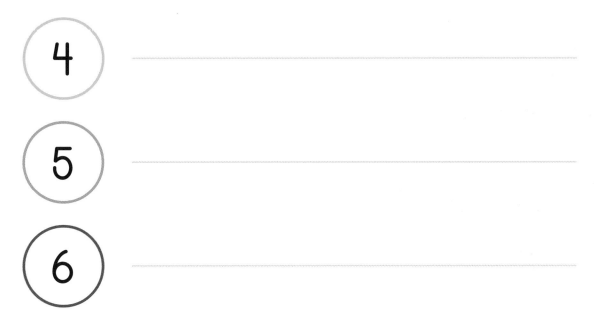

4 _____

5 _____

6 _____

How many candies are there? Write the answer.

Compte les friandises et écris ta réponse :

Your answer:

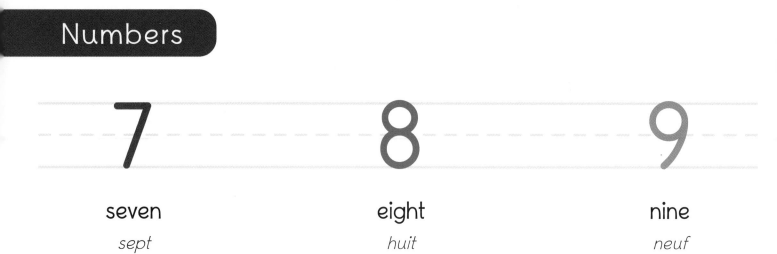

7   8   9

seven   **eight**   **nine**

sept   *huit*   *neuf*

Practice writing the number words:

Exerce-toi à écrire le nom des chiffres :

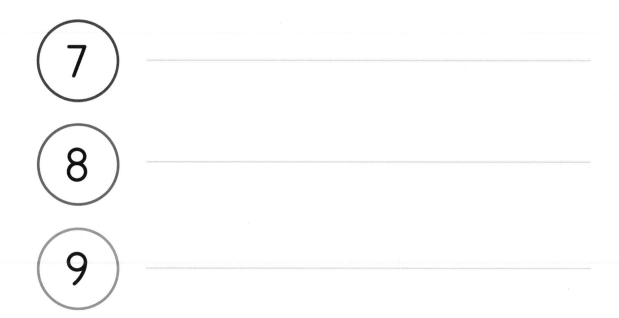

7

8

9

How many fish are there? Write the answer.

Compte les poissons et écris ta réponse :

Your answer:

10	11	12
ten	eleven	twelve
dix	*onze*	*douze*

Practice writing the number words:

Exerce-toi à écrire le nom des nombres :

10

11

12

How many shells are there? Write the answer.

Compte les coquillages et écris ta réponse :

Your answer:

13   14   15

thirteen   **fourteen**   **fifteen**

treize   *quatorze*   *quinze*

Practice writing the number words:

Exerce-toi à écrire le nom des nombres :

(13) ....

(14) ....

(15) ....

Count the flowers and circle the correct answer.

Compte les fleurs et encercle la bonne réponse.

11   12   13

16
sixteen
seize

17
seventeen
dix-sept

18
eighteen
dix-huit

Practice writing the number words:

Exerce-toi à écrire le nom des nombres :

16 _____

17 _____

18 _____

How many tires do you see? Write the answer.

Compte les pneus que tu vois et écris ta réponse :

Your answer:

19

nineteen

dix-neuf

20

twenty

vingt

Practice writing the number words:

Exerce-toi à écrire le nom des nombres :

(19) ....

(20) ....

Connect the numbers from 1 to 25.

Relie les nombres de 1 à 25.

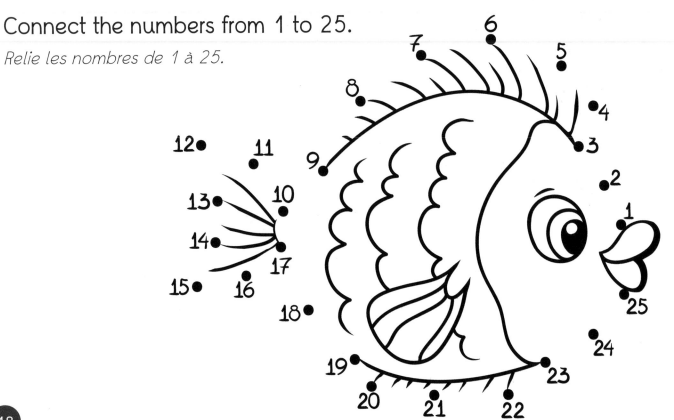

Color the squares in blue and the circles in red.

Colorie les carrés en bleu et les cercles en rouge.

Shapes

Write the shape names.

Écris le nom des formes.

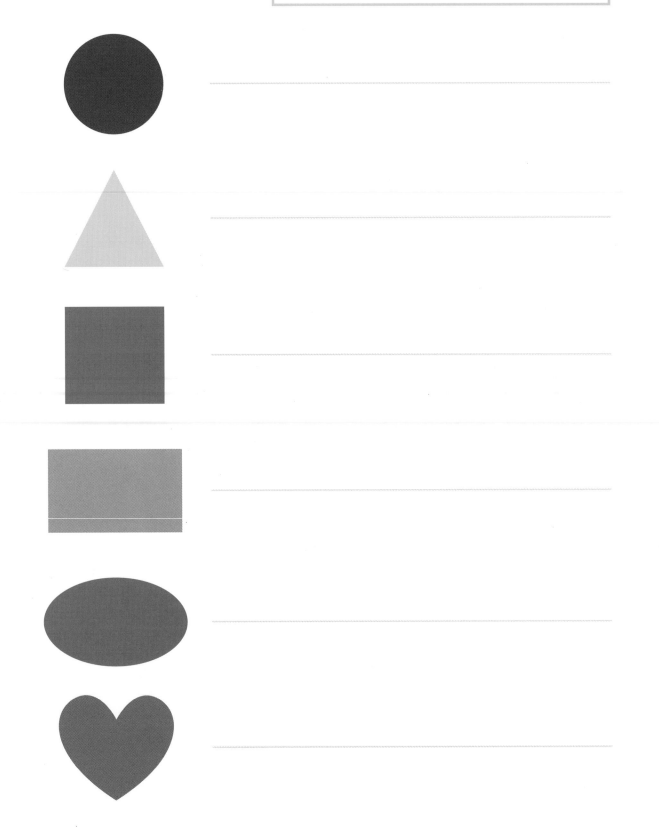

Connect the shapes to their name.

Relie les formes à leur nom.

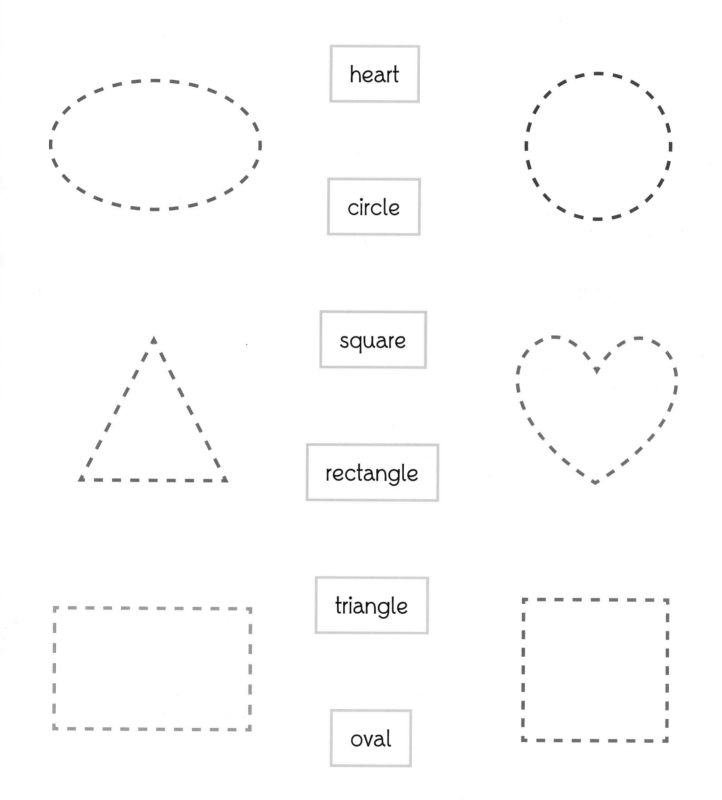

heart

circle

square

rectangle

triangle

oval

Write the name of the season and the months in the season.

Écris le nom de la saison et des mois correspondants.

WINTER
January • February • March

season

_____

months

_____

_____

_____

Draw a snowman with a scarf and a hat.

Dessine un bonhomme de neige avec une écharpe et un chapeau.

hat

scarf

Write the name of the season and the months in the season.

Écris le nom de la saison et des mois correspondants.

SPRING
April • May • June

season

_____

months

_____

_____

_____

Color in 6 watering cans.

Colorie 6 arrosoirs.

watering can   shovel   flower pot

Write the name of the season and the months in the season.

Écris le nom de la saison et des mois correspondants.

SUMMER
July • August • September

season

_____

months

_____

_____

_____

Color the rooster.

Colorie le coq.

Write the name of the season and the months in the season.

Écris le nom de la saison et des mois correspondants.

FALL
October • November • December

season

_____

months

_____

_____

Color in five leaves in orange.

Color in five leaves in orange.

Verbs

Connect each picture with the right word.

Relie chaque image au bon mot.

reading

jumping

walking

dancing

Connect each picture with the right word.

Relie chaque image au bon mot.

eating

laughing

playing

running

Find the verbs from the list to discover the hidden verb.

Trouve les verbes de la liste dans la grille pour découvrir le verbe caché.

COLOR

COOK

CRY

CUT

DANCE

DRAW

DRINK

EAT

LOOK

SING

SWIM

WALK

WRITE

W	A	L	K	Y	R	C
R	C	R	O	L	O	C
I	O	C	W	A	R	D
T	O	U	S	T	D	L
E	K	T	L	A	R	O
D	A	N	C	E	I	O
G	N	I	S	E	N	K
S	W	I	M	E	K	P

Your answer:

_____

Connect robots that have arms up with the word **UP,** and those with arms down with the word **DOWN.**

Relie les robots qui ont les bras vers le haut avec le mot UP, et ceux avec les bras vers le bas avec le mot DOWN.

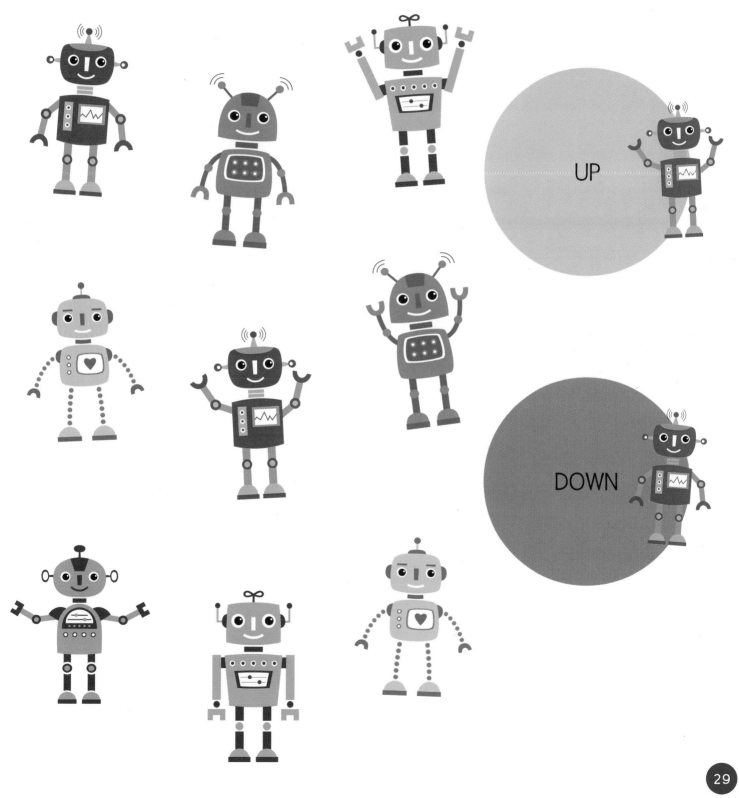

Opposites

Connect each picture to the right word.

Relie chaque image au bon mot.

hot

cold

tall

short

fast

slow

Connect each picture to the right word.

Relie chaque image au bon mot.

night

day

small

big

happy

sad

Human body

Fill in the number for each body part using the list of words.

Écris les numéros de chaque partie du corps en suivant la liste de mots.

1. hair   2. ear   3. forehead   4. eye
5. mouth   6. nose   7. cheek   8. neck

Fill in the number for each body part using the list of words.

Écris les numéros de chaque partie du corps en suivant la liste de mots.

> 1. head   2. arm   3. elbow   4. hand
> 5. finger   6. knee   7. leg   8. foot

In the city

Write the name next to each picture.

Écris le mot à côté de l'image.

street • sidewalk • building • traffic lights • crosswalk • school • schoolbus

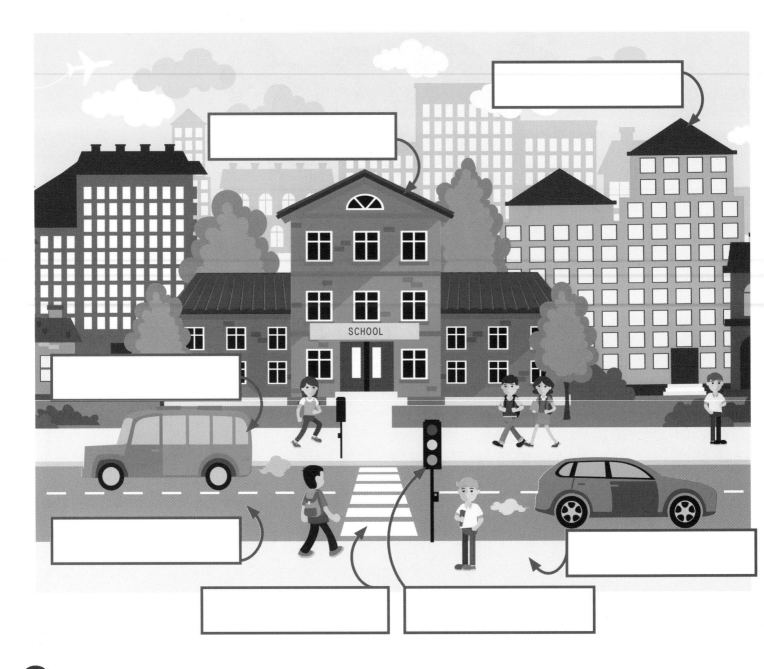

Write the correct number next to each word.

Écris le bon numéro à côté de chaque mot.

( ) window   ( ) mailbox   ( ) garage

( ) roof   ( ) porch   ( ) grass

( ) front door   ( ) tree   ( ) stairs

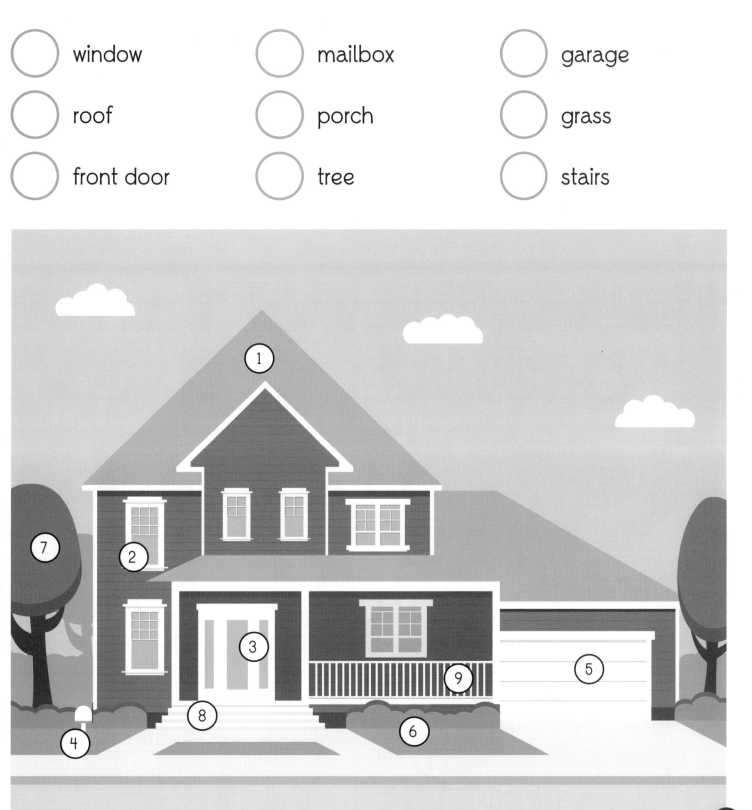

Write the correct number next to each word.

Écris le bon numéro à côté de chaque mot.

( ) fridge   ( ) knife   ( ) pot

( ) microwave   ( ) plate   ( ) drawer

( ) oven   ( ) kettle   ( ) oven mitt

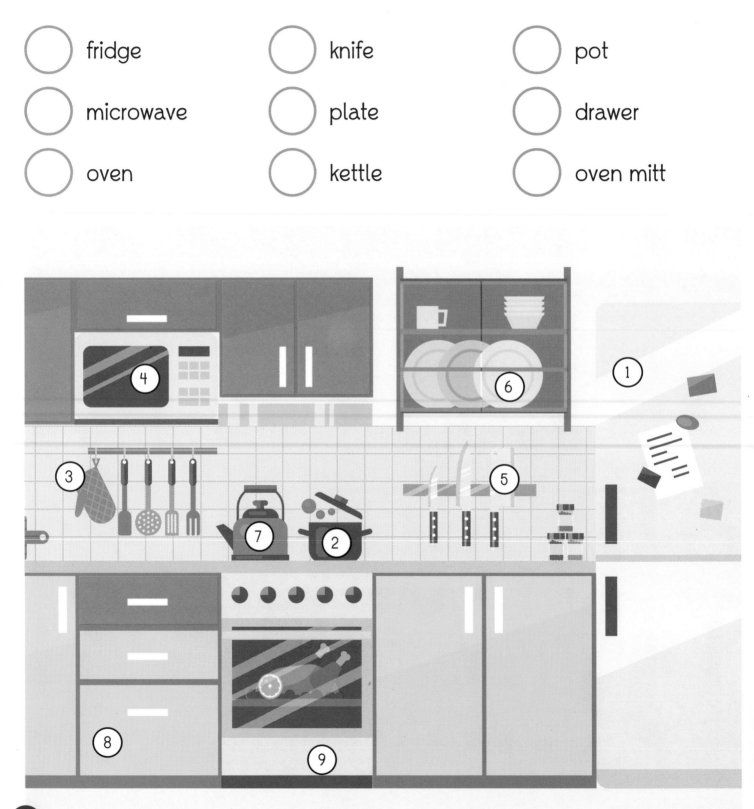

Find two things that don't belong in a kitchen.

Trouve deux objets qui ne vont pas dans une cuisine.

Connect each picture to the right word.

Relie chaque image au bon mot.

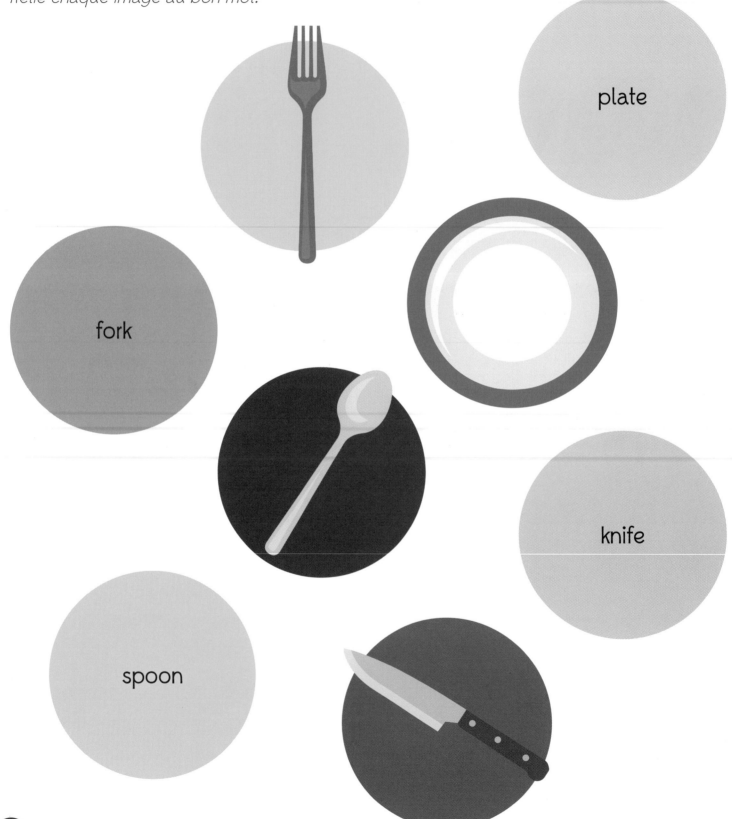

plate

fork

knife

spoon

Connect each picture to the right word.

Relie chaque image au bon mot.

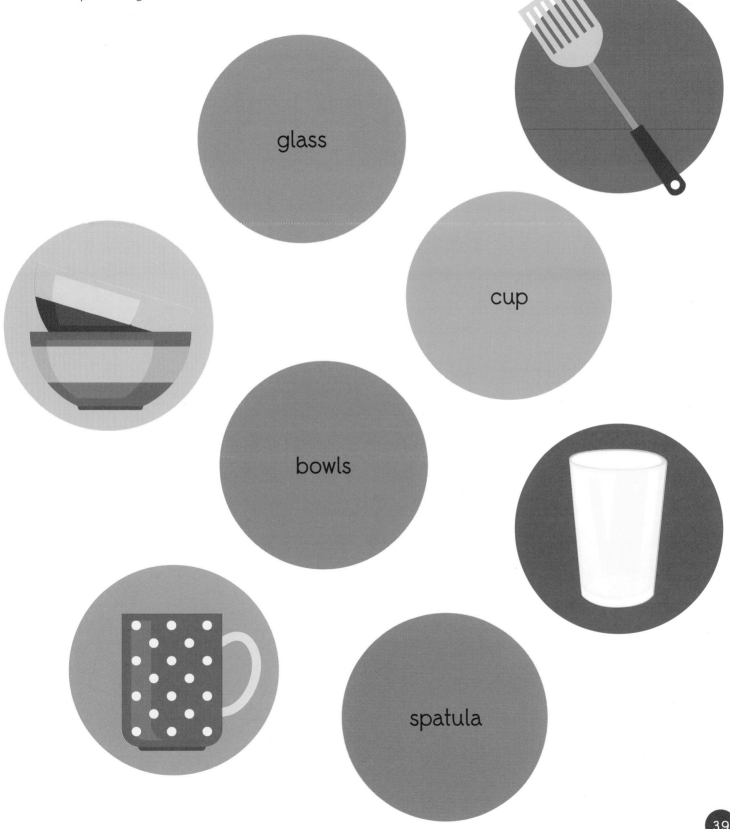

glass

cup

bowls

spatula

The bedroom

Color the objects found in the bedroom and write their names.

Colorie les objets de la chambre et écris leur nom.

pajamas • slippers • teddy bear • pillow • lamp • book • alarm clock • blanket

Circle the slippers pointing to the LEFT.

Encercle les pantoufles qui vont vers la gauche.

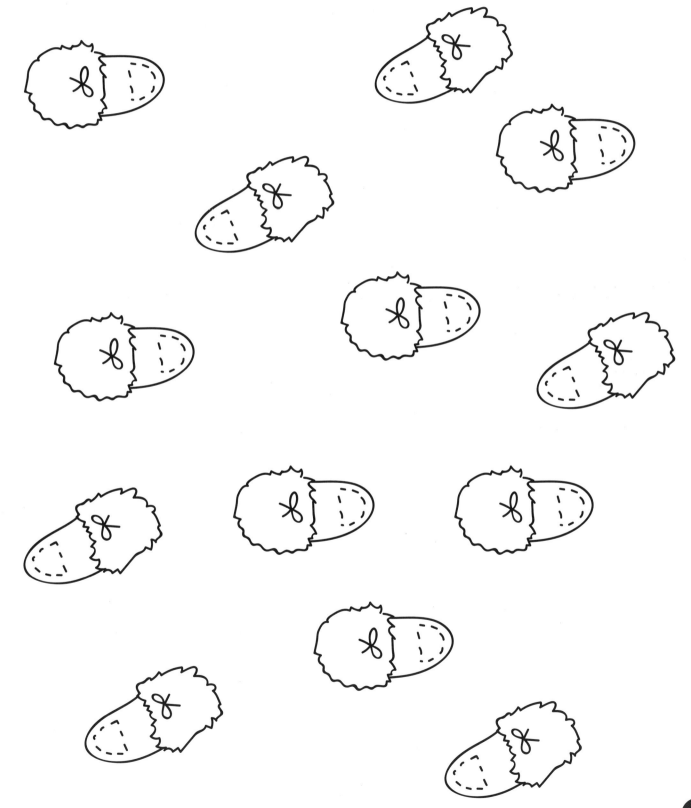

Connect each picture to the right word.

Relie chaque image au bon mot.

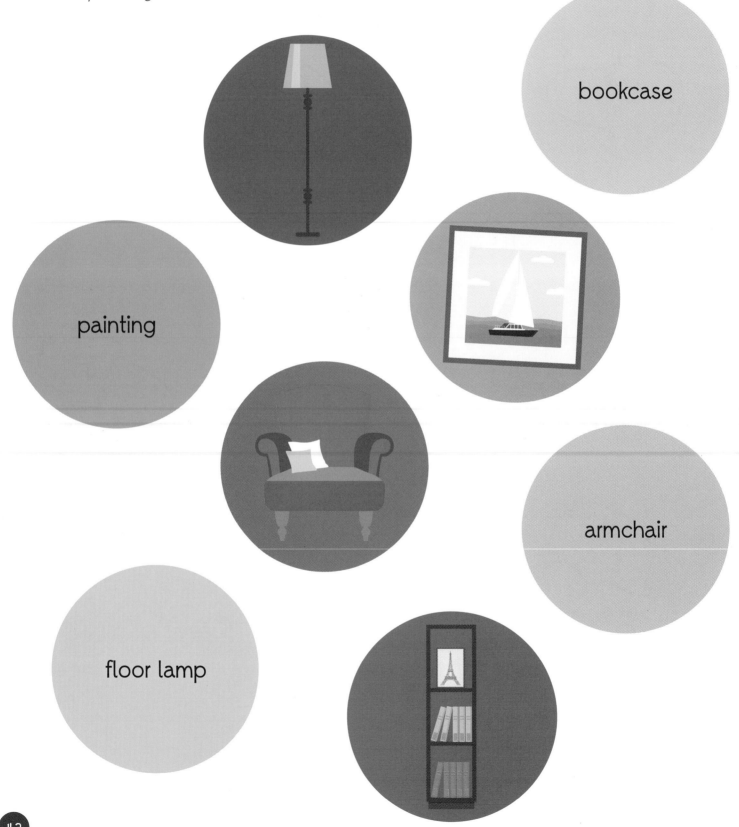

bookcase

painting

armchair

floor lamp

Connect each picture to the right word.

Relie chaque image au bon mot.

fireplace

table

cushions

sofa

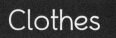
Clothes

Color the clothes the same color as their names.

Colorie les vêtements de la même couleur que leur nom.

skirt

shoes

gloves

coat

boots

Color the clothes the same color as their names.

Colorie les vêtements de la même couleur que leur nom.

dress

shirt

t-shirt

pants

Clothes

Write the names of the clothes.
Écris les noms des vêtements.

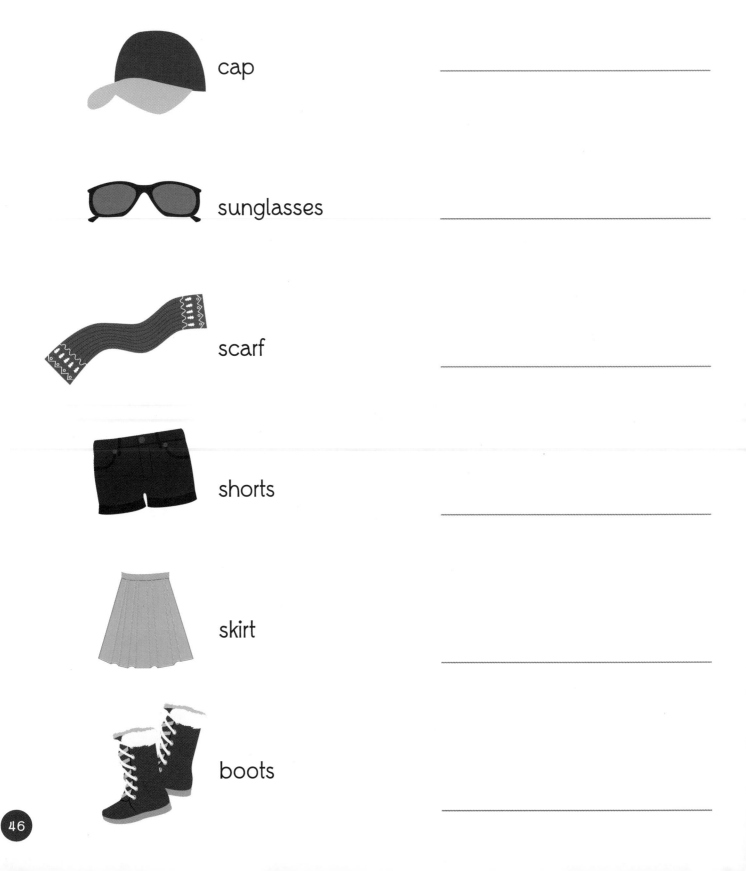

cap

sunglasses

scarf

shorts

skirt

boots

Match the clothes with the right season.

Relie les vêtements à la bonne saison.

swimsuit

sandals

toque

sock

SUMMER

gloves

hat

WINTER

t-shirt

mittens

wool vest

coat

Birthdays

Write the missing words in the invitation.

Écris les mots manquants dans la carte d'invitation.

Saturday	chocolate	noon	invite	birthday

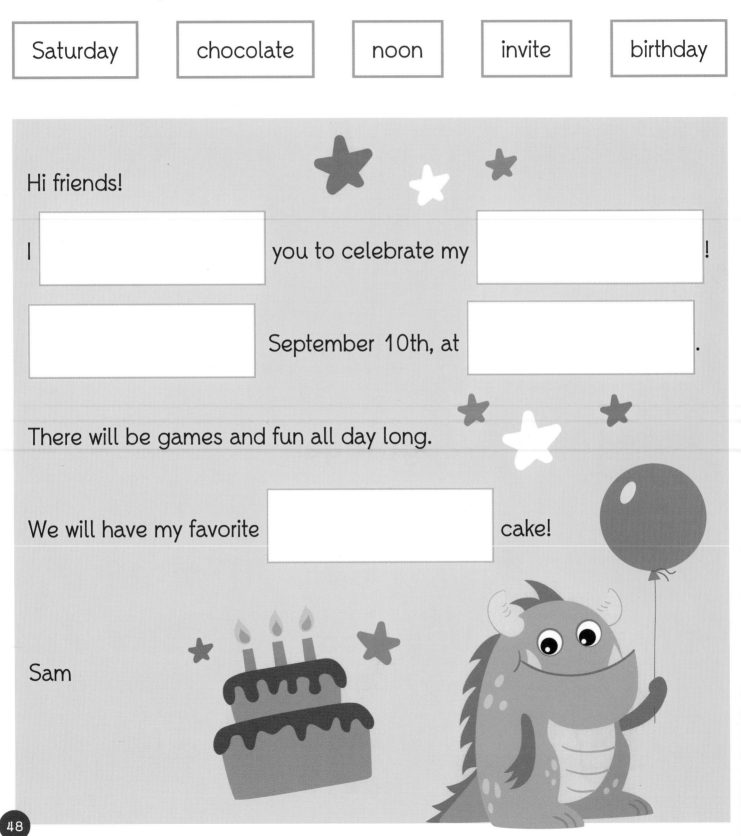

Hi friends!

I _____ you to celebrate my _____!

_____ September 10th, at _____.

There will be games and fun all day long.

We will have my favorite _____ cake!

Sam

Color in the Easter egg following the example.

Colorie l'œuf de Pâques en suivant le modèle.

Color in the picture.

Colorie l'image.

Color in the picture.

Colorie l'image.

Color five hearts in red.

Colorie cinq cœurs en rouge.

Color the pumpkins in orange and the other pictures in the color of your choice.

Colorie les citrouilles en orange et les autres images de la couleur de ton choix.

What is your favorite costume?

Fruits

Write the names of the fruits.

Écris le nom des fruits.

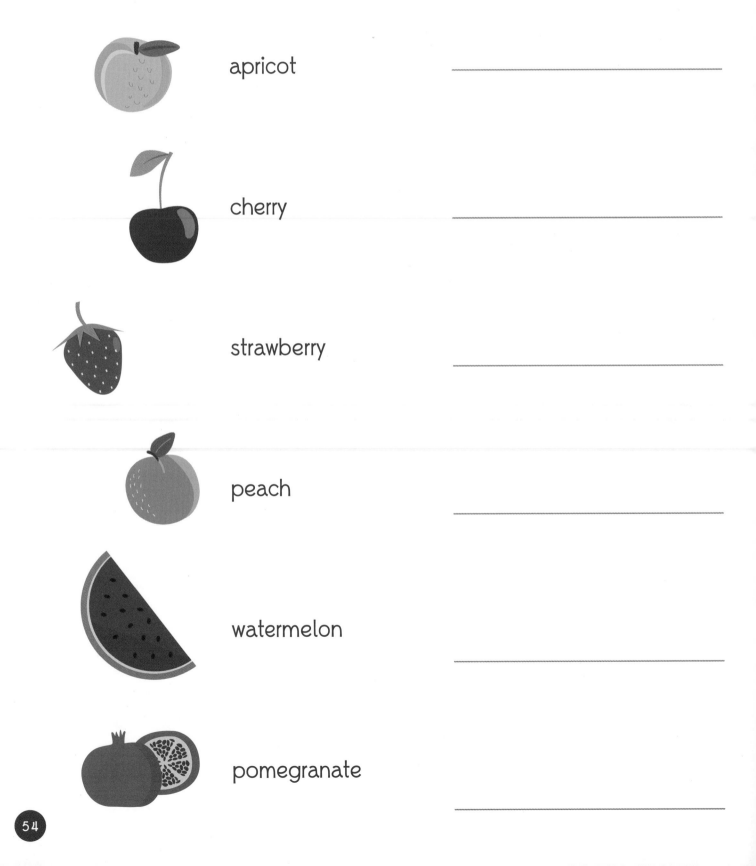

apricot

_____

cherry

_____

strawberry

_____

peach

_____

watermelon

_____

pomegranate

_____

Connect each fruit to the right color.

Relie les fruits à la bonne couleur.

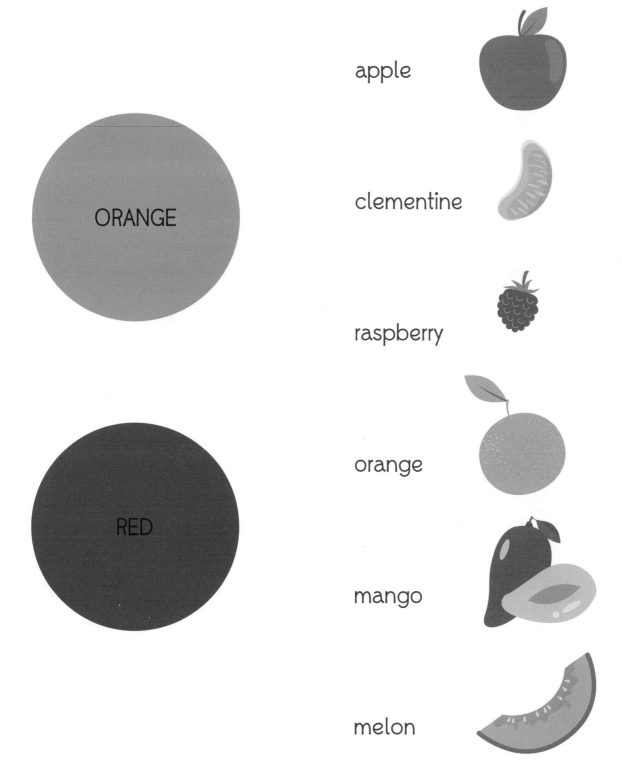

apple

ORANGE

clementine

raspberry

orange

RED

mango

melon

Connect each word to the right picture.

Relie le mot à la bonne image.

banana

coconut

lemon

pineapple

pear

grapes

blackberry

papaya

Color in the pictures that contain the letters of the word P U M P K I N.

Colorie les images qui contiennent les lettres du mot PUMPKIN.

Write the names of the vegetables.

Écris le nom des légumes.

eggplant

_____

pumpkin

_____

zucchini

_____

tomato

_____

peas

_____

broccoli

_____

Circle the green vegetables.

Encercle les légumes verts.

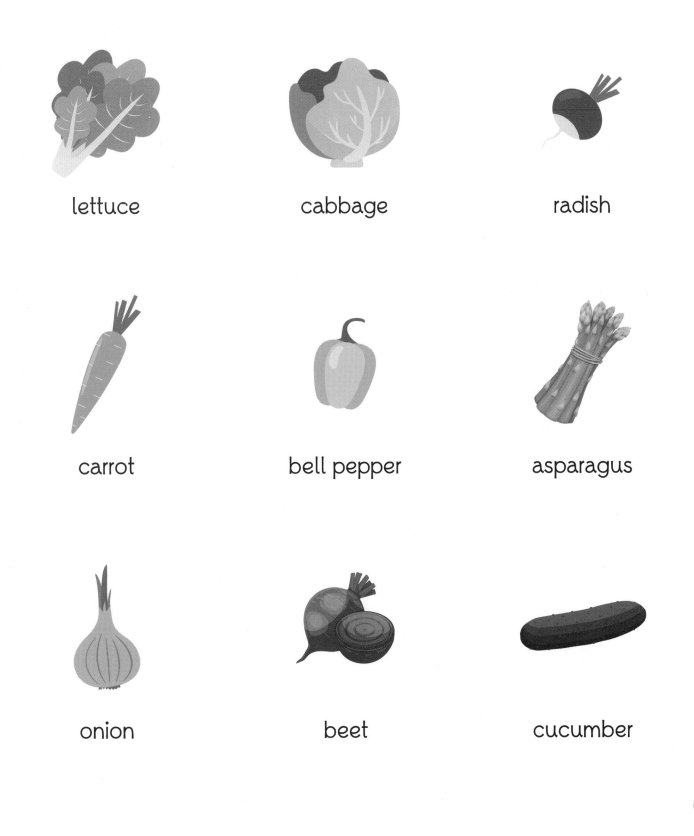

lettuce cabbage radish

carrot bell pepper asparagus

onion beet cucumber

Connect each word to the right picture.

Relie le mot à la bonne image.

mushroom

corn

potato

cauliflower

asparagus

beet

celery

onion

Draw the path following the sequence in order.

Trace le chemin en suivant la suite jusqu'à la sortie.

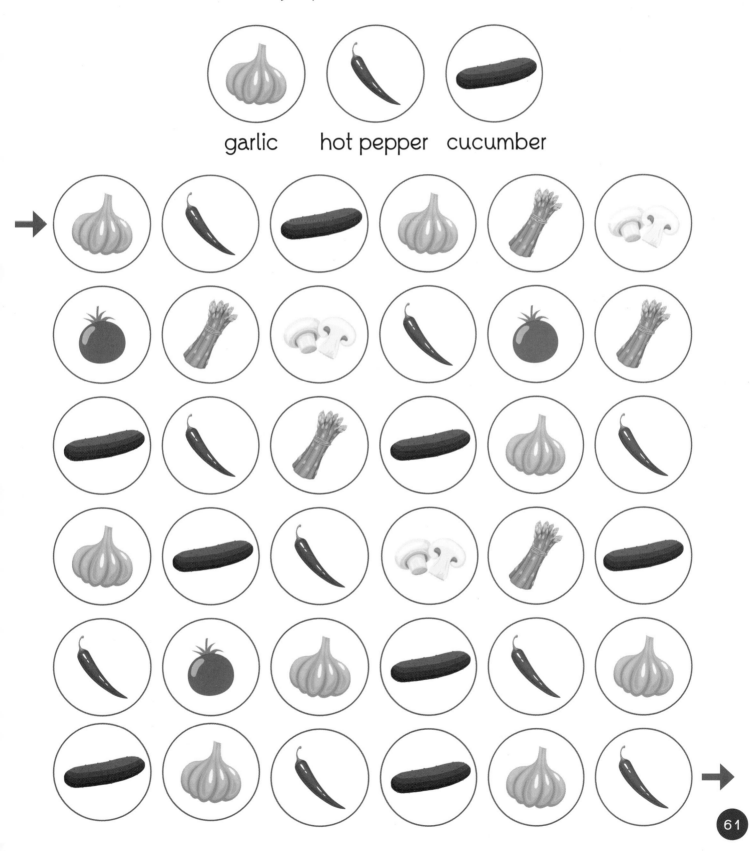

garlic   hot pepper   cucumber

Basic ingredients

Finish the sentences with the right ingredients.

Complète la phrase avec le bon ingrédient.

| flour | eggs | oil | vinegar | sugar |

| salt | pepper | milk |

To season my dishes, I use ☐ and ☐ .

In my omelet, I put 4 ☐ .

I use white ☐ to make pie dough.

To make salad dressing, I mix ☐ and ☐ .

I put ☐ in my cereal.

In lemonade, there is lemon and ☐ .

At the restaurant, you can order your favorite dishes.
Choose what you like to eat from the menu and write it on the list.

Au restaurant, tu peux commander tes plats préférés.
Choisis dans le menu ce que tu aimes manger et écris-le sur la liste.

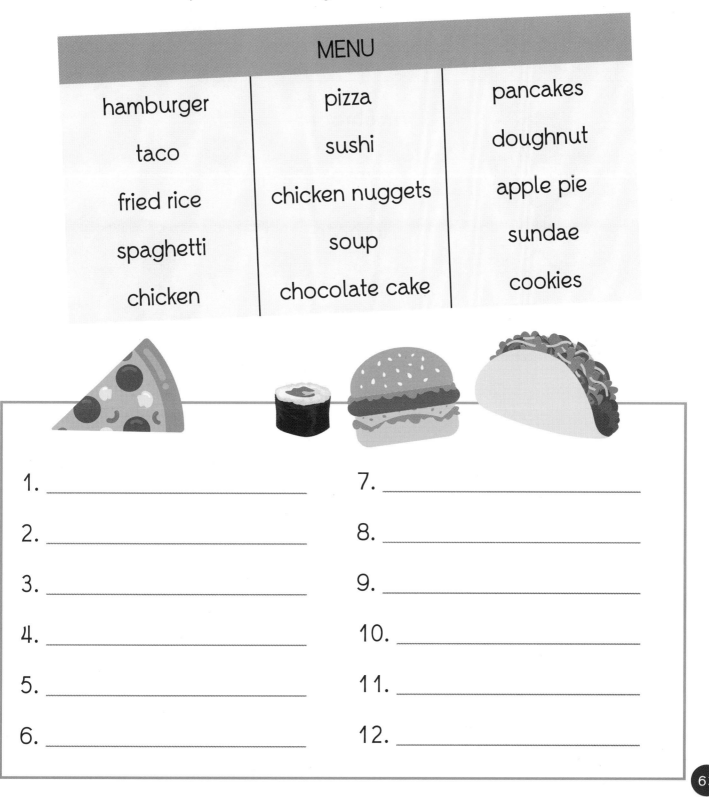

MENU

hamburger	pizza	pancakes
taco	sushi	doughnut
fried rice	chicken nuggets	apple pie
spaghetti	soup	sundae
chicken	chocolate cake	cookies

1. _____

2. _____

3. _____

4. _____

5. _____

6. _____

7. _____

8. _____

9. _____

10. _____

11. _____

12. _____

Food

Cross out the things that should not be eaten.

Barre les éléments qui ne peuvent être mangés.

plane

skirt

mushroom

tree

tomato

melon

table

skate

banana

apple

button

broccoli

soup

boat

Circle the matching pairs of cupcakes. Find the one that doesn't belong!

Entoure les paires identiques de gâteaux. Puis, trouve l'intrus.

Days of the week

Write the missing days of the week on the calendar.

Écris les jours manquants sur le calendrier de la semaine.

Monday • Tuesday • Wednesday • Thursday • Friday • Saturday • Sunday

1	2	3
MONDAY		
4	5	
	FRIDAY	
6	7	

Friday is my favorite day!

66

Complete the sentences using the words from the list.

Complète les phrases en te servant de la liste de mots.

night

morning

breakfast

evening

afternoon

lunch

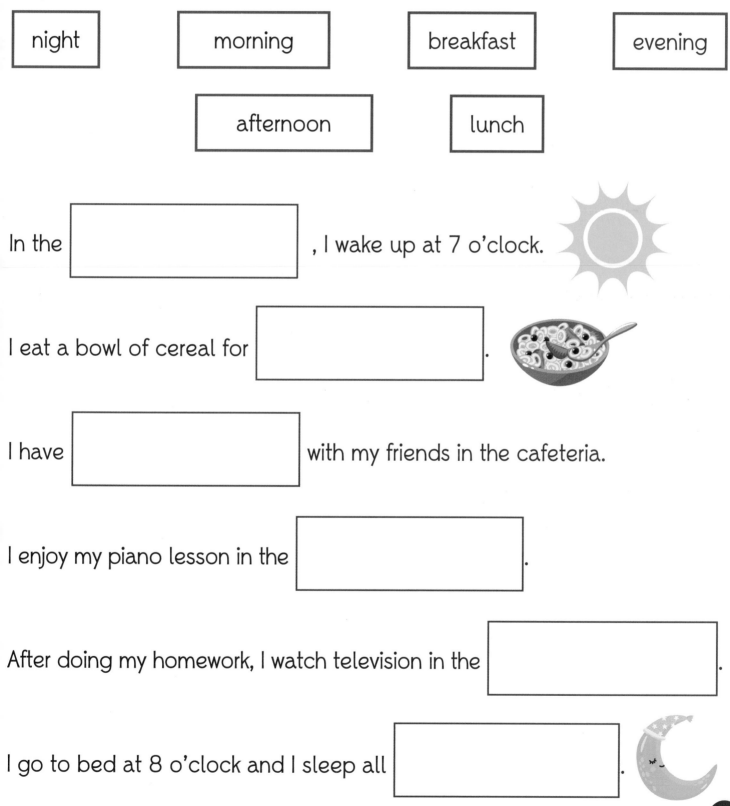

In the _____ , I wake up at 7 o'clock.

I eat a bowl of cereal for _____ .

I have _____ with my friends in the cafeteria.

I enjoy my piano lesson in the _____ .

After doing my homework, I watch television in the _____ .

I go to bed at 8 o'clock and I sleep all _____ .

Complete the names of the tools.

Complète les noms des outils.

saw • drill • nail • wrench

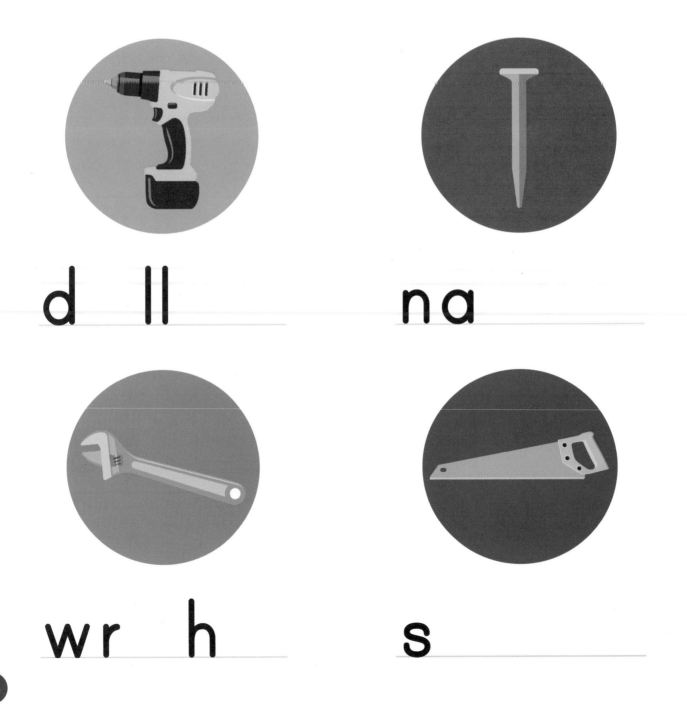

d __ ll __

na __ __

wr __ h __

s __ __

Complete the names of the tools.

Complète les noms des outils.

hammer • screwdriver • pliers • screw

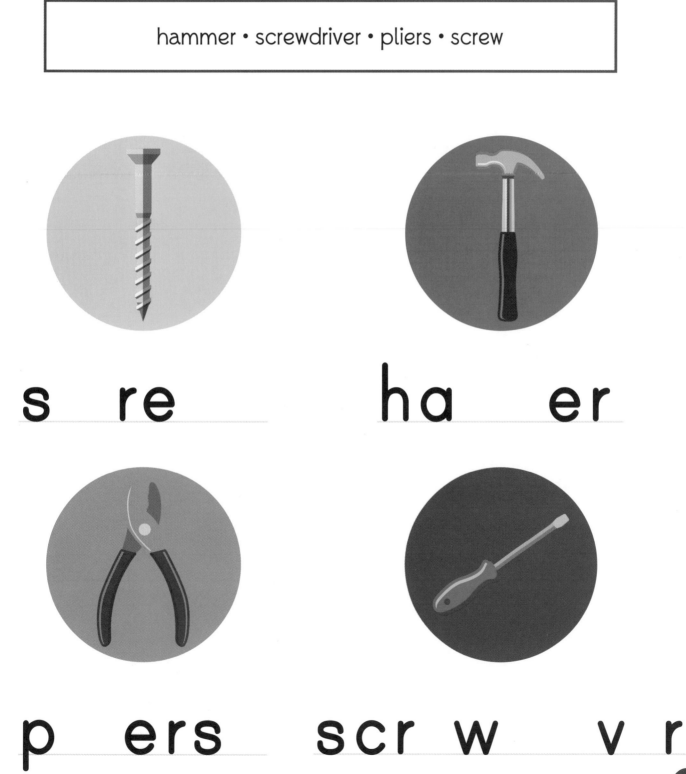

s   re

ha   er

p   ers

scr w   v r

Circle the matching pairs of schoolbags. Find the one that doesn't belong!

Entoure les paires identiques de sacs à dos. Puis, trouve l'intrus.

Circle the buses going to the RIGHT.

Encercle les autobus qui vont vers la droite.

Connect each word to the right picture.

Relie le mot à la bonne image.

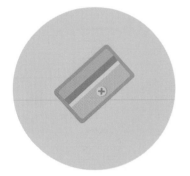

schoolbag

notebook

pencil

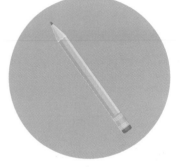

colored pencils

scissors

pencil sharpener

eraser

glue

Musical instruments

Write the name of the musical instruments under each musician.

Écris le nom des instruments de musique sous chaque musicien.

violin • drum • guitar •
flute • maracas • cymbals

Color the maracas however you like.

Colorie les maracas à ton goût.

Things that go

Write the name of each vehicle using the list of words.

Écris le nom de chaque véhicule en te servant de la liste de mots.

car • truck • fire truck • rocket • bicycle • boat •
helicopter • scooter • sailboat

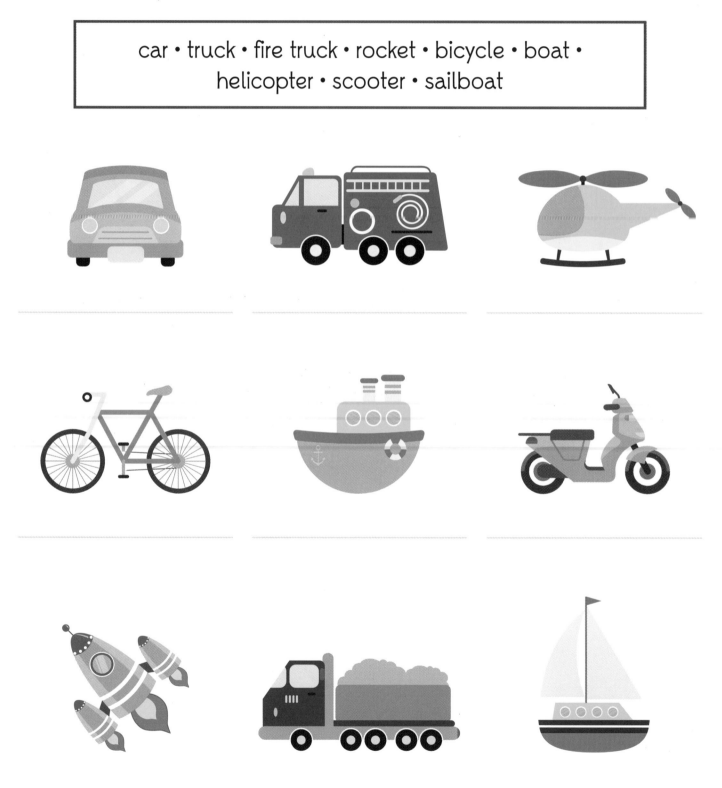

Write the name of each vehicle using the list of words.

Écris le nom de chaque véhicule en te servant de la liste de mots.

> bus • plane • train • submarine • motorcycle • wagon •
> police car • ambulance • air balloon

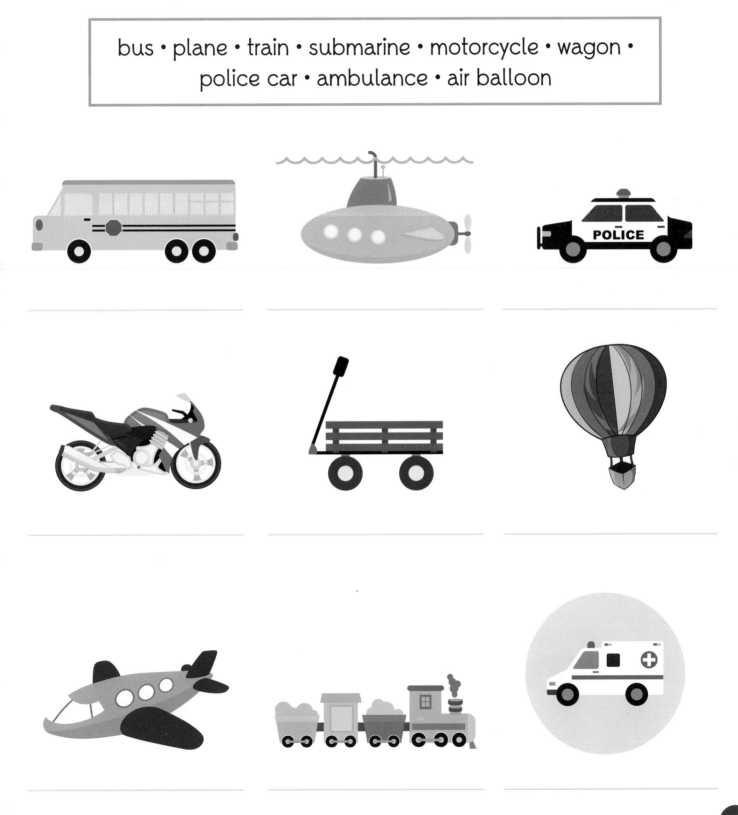

Sports

Match each picture with the right word.

Relie chaque image au bon mot.

ice skating

swimming

tennis

soccer

karate

hockey

skiing

basketball

Write the right action verb under each picture.

Écris le bon verbe en dessous de chaque image.

> skating • riding a bicycle • kicking a ball • skipping rope • dribbling a ball • playing badminton

Toys and games

Write the names of the toys and games using the list of words.

Écris le nom des jouets et des jeux en te servant de la liste de mots.

> teddy bear • doll • spinning top • blocks • skipping rope •
> jigsaw puzzle • playing cards • bowling pins • robot

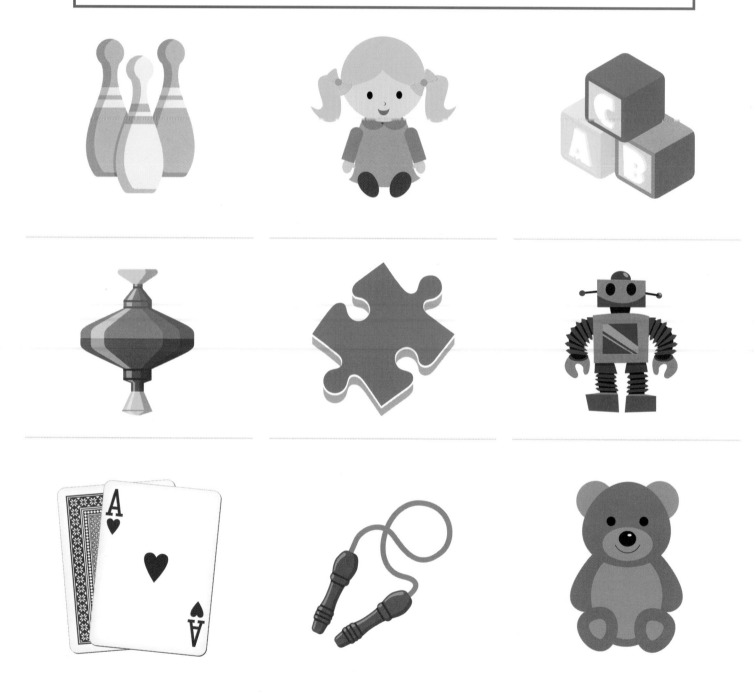

Circle the matching pairs of toys. Find the one that doesn't belong!

Entoure les paires identiques de jouets. Puis, trouve l'intrus.

Pets

Write the names of each animal using the list of words.

Écris le nom de chaque animal en te servant de la liste de mots.

> cat • dog • rabbit • hamster •
> bird • turtle • guinea pig • fish • hedgehog

Draw a cat step-by-step.

Dessine le chat étape par étape.

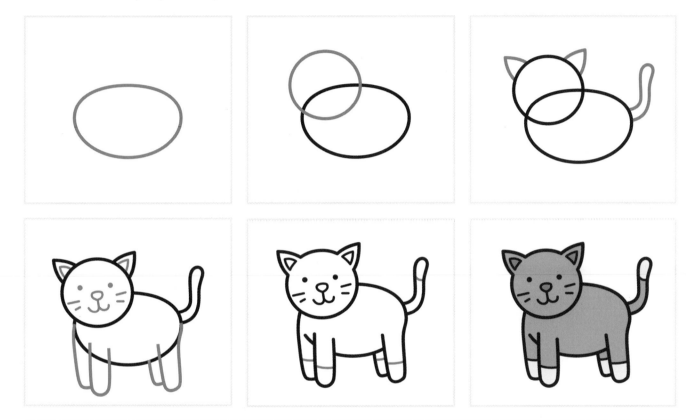

Farm animals

Practice writing the animal words.

Exerce-toi à écrire le nom des animaux.

> cow • horse • pig • sheep • goat •
> duck • donkey • bull • goose

What do you find in a chicken coop?

Que trouves-tu dans un poulailler ?

> hen • rooster • chicks • hay • eggs

How many chicks are there? Write the answer.

Compte les poussins et écris ta réponse :

Your answer:

Zoo animals

Find all the animal names hidden in the grid.

Trouve les noms des animaux dans la grille.

CAMEL
ELEPHANT
GIRAFFE
KANGAROO

LION
MONKEY
PANDA
PEACOCK

RHINOCEROS
TIGER
ZEBRA

P	C	O	O	R	A	G	N	A	K
E	E	L	E	P	H	A	N	T	L
A	A	L	I	O	N	R	B	I	E
C	D	Q	V	X	M	B	C	G	M
O	N	M	O	N	K	E	Y	E	A
C	A	F	G	A	D	Z	X	R	C
K	P	W	G	I	R	A	F	F	E
S	O	R	E	C	O	N	I	H	R

Help the lion cub find his way through the maze.

Aide le lionceau à trouver son chemin à travers le labyrinthe.

Write the correct number next to each picture.

Écris le numéro correspondant à côté de chaque image.

(1) fox   (4) squirrel   (7) raccoon

(2) wolf   (5) rabbit   (8) bear

(3) deer   (6) owl   (9) mouse

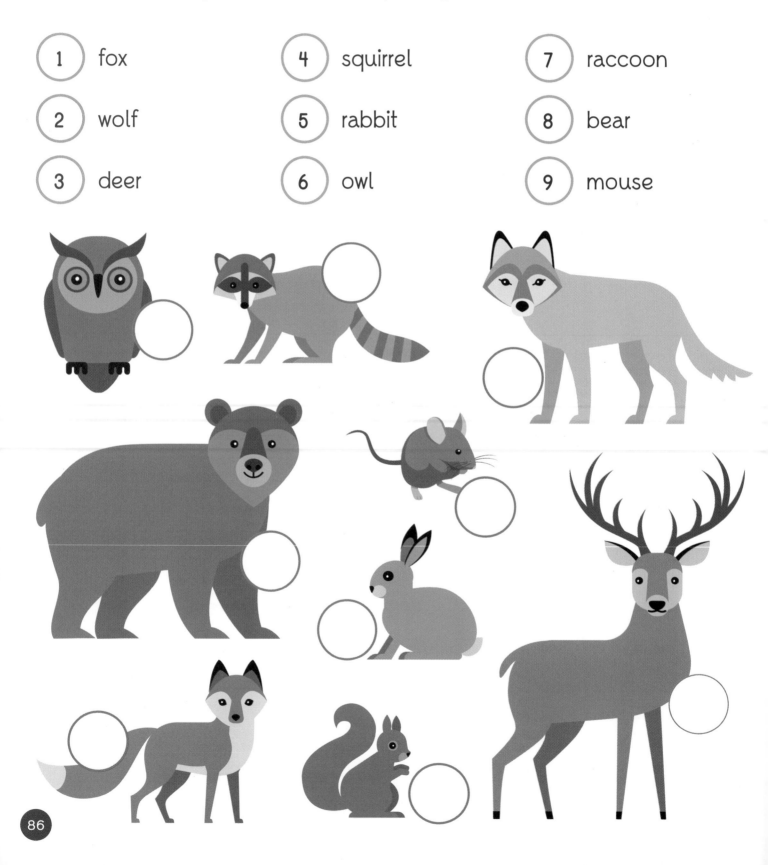

Help the bear find his mother.

Aide l'ourson à trouver sa maman.

Sea animals

Find all the sea animal names hidden in the grid.

Trouve les noms des animaux de la mer dans la grille.

SQUID	SHARK	JELLYFISH
RAY	WHALE	OCTOPUS
BELUGA	SHRIMP	STARFISH
CRAB	LOBSTER	SEAHORSE

S	H	S	I	F	Y	L	L	E	J
T	R	H	X	B	E	L	U	G	A
A	E	R	S	U	P	O	T	C	O
R	T	I	Z	X	C	R	A	B	H
F	S	M	W	H	A	L	E	Q	Z
I	B	P	Q	Z	K	R	A	H	S
S	O	R	A	Y	S	Q	U	I	D
H	L	E	S	R	O	H	A	E	S

Circle the matching pairs of fish. Find the one that doesn't belong!

Entoure les paires identiques de poissons. Puis, trouve l'intrus.

Insects

Practice writing the insect words.

Exerce-toi à écrire le nom des insectes.

> bee • butterfly • mosquito • fly • ladybug •
> wasp • dragonfly • grasshopper • ant

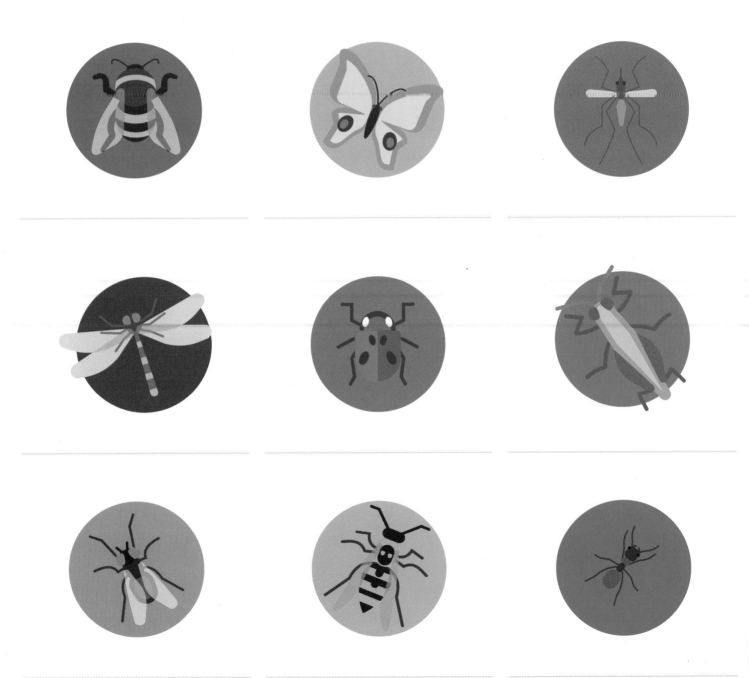

Help the bee, the ladybug and the butterfly find their friends.

Aide l'abeille, la coccinelle et le papillon à trouver leurs amis.

Quiz

Find the answers and connect them to the right picture.

Trouve les réponses et relie-les à la bonne image.

- I can fly.
- You can count my black dots
- My wings are red.

- You have two of them.
- They are very useful for seeing.
- They can be of different colors.

- You use it in the kitchen.
- It is useful to eat your cereal.
- It can be small or big.

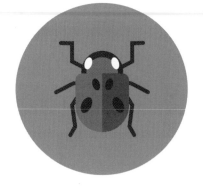

- I can fly.
- I can transport people.
- I have a powerful engine.

Follow the secret code to find the message.

Suis le code secret et découvre le message.

!

Word Index

NUMBERS

1 one
2 two
3 three
4 four
5 five
6 six
7 seven
8 eight
9 nine
10 ten
11 eleven
12 twelve
13 thirteen
14 fourteen
15 fifteen
16 sixteen
17 seventeen
18 eighteen
19 nineteen
20 twelve

COLORS

 black
blue
brown
green
orange

pink
purple
red
white
yellow

MONTHS AND SEASONS

 **Winter:** January February March

 **Summer:** July August September

Spring: April May June

 **Fall:** October November December

HUMAN BODY

arm bras
cheek joue
ear oreille
elbow coude
eyes yeux
finger doigt
foot pied
forehead front

hair cheveux
hand main
head tête
knee genou
leg jambe
mouth bouche
neck cou
nose nez

94

PETS

bird oiseau

cat chat

dog chien

fish poisson

guinea pig cochon d'inde

hamster hamster

rabbit lapin

turtle tortue

ZOO ANIMALS

camel chameau

elephant éléphant

giraffe girafe

kangaroo kangourou

lion lion

monkey singe

panda panda

peacock paon

rhinoceros rhinocéros

tiger tigre

zebra zèbre

FARM ANIMALS

chick poussin

cow vache

donkey âne

goat chèvre

hen poule

horse cheval

pig cochon

rooster coq

sheep mouton

FOREST ANIMALS

bear ours

deer cerf

fox renard

frog grenouille

owl hibou

squirrel écureuil

wolf loup

woodpecker pic

INSECTS

ant fourmi

bee abeille

butterfly papillon

dragonfly libellule

fly mouche

grasshopper sauterelle

ladybug coccinelle

mosquito moustique

spider araignée

wasp guêpe

I AM LEARNING
ENGLISH

DIPLOMA
Congratulations!
You have successfully finished your activities.

_____

Name

_____

Date

_____

Signature